Magical Myths and Legends

Chosen By

MICHAEL
MORPURGO

This book belongs to:

_____

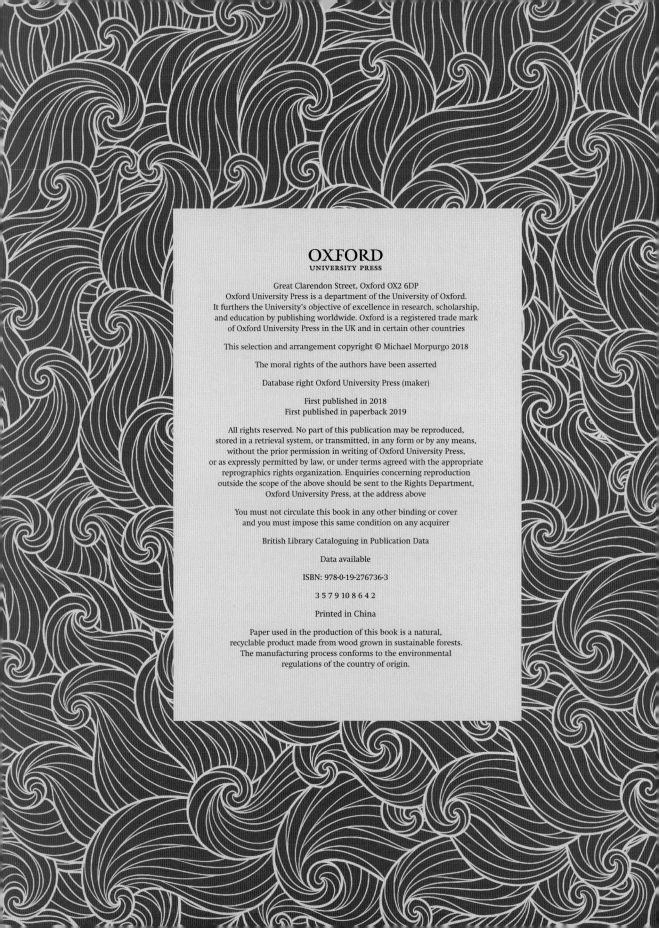

OXFORD
UNIVERSITY PRESS

Great Clarendon Street, Oxford OX2 6DP

Oxford University Press is a department of the University of Oxford.
It furthers the University's objective of excellence in research, scholarship,
and education by publishing worldwide. Oxford is a registered trade mark
of Oxford University Press in the UK and in certain other countries

Database right Oxford University Press (maker)

First published in 2018
First published in paperback 2019

British Library Cataloguing in Publication Data

Data available

ISBN: 978-0-19-276736-3

3 5 7 9 10 8 6 4 2

Printed in China

Paper used in the production of this book is a natural,
recyclable product made from wood grown in sustainable forests.
The manufacturing process conforms to the environmental
regulations of the country of origin.

Magical Myths and Legends

Chosen By

MICHAEL MORPURGO

OXFORD

UNIVERSITY PRESS

Introduction

It is difficult to imagine now that there was a time before books, before radio, before theatre and television and film, before downloading movies on to computers and iPads. These days we can have our stories any way we like. There are so many ways that we can discover and enjoy our stories. But for thousands of years stories were told and passed around only by word of mouth. Storytelling was the only way it could be done. Stories might be spoken or sung or danced or acted out, but for the most part they were simply told.

All the myths and legends you can read in this book have evolved over the centuries. The origins of all of them are mostly lost in the mists of time, often before history as we know it began. This is the era of myths and legends, all of which have roots in the lives of our forebears hundreds of years ago, and which were told by them, passed on by grandfather to child, mother to child.

Every one of these myths has had thousands upon thousands of tellers over the years, so that each time a story is told, it is never the same. There is a new voice every time. And even when our ancestors first began to write them down, only a few hundred years ago, the storytellers went on changing them. But these stories are for us a direct link to them.

So when you read in this book the stories of Robin Hood or King Arthur, when you read of the great heroes of Greek myths, or Irish legends, you are reading the stories they knew and loved. You are reading simply the latest telling of many. And when you tell it yourself—which you might like to do—you will tell it your way, and so the legend grows, the same story, but told and woven differently. All these myths and legends are constantly changing, constantly renewed.

What is extraordinary is how these legends have lasted, have been enriched by all this retelling, been remade, refreshed, and transformed by book and theatre and film, so that each new generation can enjoy the stories our ancestors knew and loved around the hearth and home all those years ago. Their heroes, their stories, have become our heroes, our stories.

Michael Morpurgo

Contents

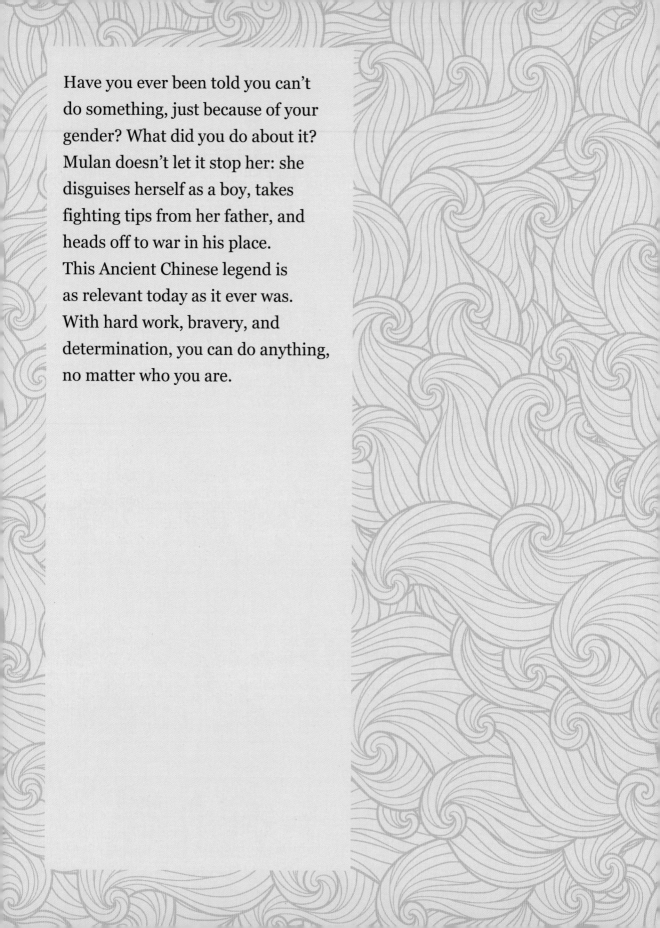

Have you ever been told you can't do something, just because of your gender? What did you do about it? Mulan doesn't let it stop her: she disguises herself as a boy, takes fighting tips from her father, and heads off to war in his place.
This Ancient Chinese legend is as relevant today as it ever was. With hard work, bravery, and determination, you can do anything, no matter who you are.

Mulan

Retold by Michaela Morgan

Illustrated by Steve Dorado

Mulan was working quietly in her corner of the house, just as she did every day. She was at her loom, weaving, weaving. Just as she did every day.

Shhhhh, shhhhh went the shuttles of her loom.

It was quiet in the house.

Mulan's father, tired and ill, was tossing and turning in his bed. Mulan's mother, busy as ever, was making a meal. Little Brother was playing as quietly as Little Brother could.

Shhhhh, shhhhh went the shuttles of the loom. But there was another sound. What was it?

It was the sound of Mulan sighing as she worked.

'What is it?' Father asked her.

'Why do you sigh?' Mother asked her.

'Are you dreaming of a boyfriend? Are you wishing for new shoes?' Little Brother asked her. He was a cheeky boy and liked to tease his older sister.

'I am thinking of the poster I saw in town,' said Mulan. She sighed again. 'Our country is under attack! We have been ordered to send a man from this family to fight in the Emperor's army.'

WAR!
One man from every family MUST join the army to fight for the Emperor!

'A man from our family must go to fight or we will all be punished,' sighed Mulan's father. 'I will do what has to be done.'

The sick old man tried to struggle to his feet, but he had not even the strength to stand.

'You will not last a day!' cried Mulan's mother. 'Your fighting days are over.'

'I will go instead of Father!' said Little Brother. He picked up his tiny wooden sword and pretended to fight his toys. But he whirled his toy sword so quickly that he lost his footing and fell down. Oof!

Mulan looked at her little brother lying in his pile of toys. He was still clutching his toy sword. He was much, much too young to fight for his country.

She looked at her father. He was much, much too old. True, he had once been a very skilled soldier, but those days were long gone.

'I am just the right age,' she thought. 'I can run and
ride better than many boys. I can think quickly and I
have helped Father practise his fighting skills for years.
I should be the one who joins the army.'

Mulan spoke up bravely, 'I want to buy a saddle and horse. I will go to the army in Father's place.'

How Little Brother laughed! 'Silly, silly, silly!' he said. 'You're only a soppy girl.'

How Mulan's mother fretted, 'No, no, no, it's not right. Your place is here with us. Girls are not allowed in the Emperor's army.'

Her father was too tired
and sick to say much.
He just groaned, 'No, Mulan,
nooo!'

Mulan was determined.

'I have a plan,' she said. 'I will dress like a boy. I'll wear padding and armour. They'll never know I'm a girl!'

'Impossible!' said her mother.

'Dangerous!' gasped her father.

'Crazy!' said Little Brother.

Mulan had made up her mind. She was ready to do anything to save her family.

In the East Market she went to buy a speedy horse.

In the West Market she got a saddle.

In the North Market she got a full set of armour.

In the South Market she got a sword.

At home, she tied up her hair and tried on her armour. All that night she practised her fighting skills and took tips from her father.

She no longer looked like Mulan. Now she
looked like a soldier.

At dawn she said goodbye to her father and mother, she
climbed on to the back of her speedy horse, and rode away.

'She'll be back by teatime,' laughed Little Brother.

Yet Mulan was not back by teatime that day or the next.

Mulan travelled for three days along the banks of the Yellow River. The ground was hard, the air was chill, and the nights were dark and lonely.

She missed her family and many times she wished she could go home, but bravely she went on. At dusk on the third day, she arrived at the army camp at Black Mountain.

As Mulan approached the camp a guard appeared, blocking her way.

'Where are you going?' he challenged. Mulan shivered, but she said in a deep voice, 'I am here to join the army as ordered.'

The guard nodded. Surprised, Mulan passed quickly into the camp.

From that moment on, Mulan lived in fear of her fellow

soldiers discovering she was a girl. Army life was tough and every day sights and sounds reminded her of home and her family.

The days were long.
The nights were longer.
The life was harder than hard.

Mulan didn't give up. She worked hard and she trained hard. She learned how to use a spear and how to carry a shield. She learned how to attack and defend and how to ride at the speed of the wind.

Soon it was time for the first battle.

Mulan's blood ran cold with dread and fear. Her knees shook. Her heart pounded, but she clutched her sword tightly and went into battle.

Oh, she was as brave as any soldier!
Oh, she was as quick as any runner!

And she was clever! She used her sword but she also used her brain. She outwitted her enemies.

She used her spear to leap over her attackers. She danced her way past clumsy attacks. She hid under her shield then jumped out to take her attackers by surprise.

She earned the respect of her fellow soldiers. They still had no idea she was a young girl.

They clapped her on her back and said. 'What clever tricks you use!' That was the first battle of many.

She became a fine warrior.
She became a leader.

She survived one long year,
two years, three years, four,
five and six and seven and
more.

For ten long years she
survived.

She travelled far.
She rode through great
green forests.

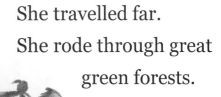

She rode across hot
red deserts.
She rode up steep and
snowy mountains.

She rode one thousand, two
thousand, three thousand miles,
four, five thousand, six thousand,
seven and more.
She travelled ten
thousand miles.

She kept her hair tied up, she kept her courage strong, and she kept her secret well. She became a famous officer and led her troops into many a successful battle.

But every night she dreamed of her home, her mother, her father, and Little Brother. She wondered how they were.

Finally the war was won. The
Emperor was pleased with
Mulan.

'You have been brave and
true,' he said. 'Ask for any
reward and you can have it.
Gold? Diamonds? Palaces?'

Mulan knew exactly what she wanted.

'I want a fast horse and I want my freedom!' she said. 'I want to leave fighting behind and return to my family to live in peace.'

Her wish was granted.

When Father and Mother heard the sound of horses' hooves they came out to look. They saw a fine officer riding towards them.

It was Mulan, followed by her troop of soldiers. She looked so splendid, riding her fine horse.

Little Brother ran out to welcome the soldiers and to cheer.

Mulan went into the house to her old rooms. She sat at her old table and she took off her armour.

She let her hair down. She washed the dust off.

She put on her dresses, long and flowing.

Then she went out of the door and greeted her troop
of soldiers.

'I am Mulan,' she said.

Her comrades were all amazed.

'A girl!' they shouted. 'Not possible!'

It took a lot of explaining before they could believe it.

The soldiers were so amazed that they told Mulan's tale far and wide. The story of how a young girl became a warrior spread from person to person, it crossed mountains and oceans to many different countries.

In Mulan's land people still sing about her.

It is hard to believe
that it could be so,
but now we have learned,
now we know
not to judge people by how they look.
You, too, can be a hero
and have your tale told
or put in a book.

If you could have a superpower, what would you choose? People often wish that they could fly, and it is a dream that has been around for thousands of years. The legend of Icarus, who flew too close to the sun, comes from Ancient Greece, before there was any thought of aeroplanes or hang-gliders. Sadly though, Icarus ignores his father's warnings, and his arrogance means that his dream of flying ends in tragedy. Would you have behaved differently if you were in Icarus's wings?

Icarus

Retold by Susan Gates

Illustrated by Joe Todd-Stanton

My name is Amara. Listen to my amazing story, children. Many years ago, when I was young like you, I flew like a bird!

I was the servant girl of Daedalus, the great inventor. Daedalus worked for Minos, the King of Crete. But one day, he made Minos angry. To punish Daedalus, Minos locked him up in a high tower.

Daedalus's son, Icarus, was locked up with him.

I lived in the tower with them. But I wasn't a prisoner. I was allowed to go out whenever I wanted.

Icarus stared out of the tower window. All he could see were rocky cliffs and waves and seagulls. He cried, 'Father! Get me out of here *now*! Or I will die of boredom!'

Escaping wasn't so easy. There were guards outside the tower door all the time.

My master thought hard, day and night, but even he had no ideas.

Icarus was bored. He paced around the tower like
a tiger in a cage. He threw a piece of bread out of the
window. Seagulls dived for it, fighting and screaming.

Suddenly, my master smiled. He said,
'Amara, I have a brilliant plan! You're not a prisoner
like us. Go out and get me lots of feathers!'

I was really puzzled. I said, 'Feathers? Why, Master?'

But Daedalus only answered, 'You'll soon see!'

I went outside. I picked up seagull feathers from the beach. I hid them under my cloak so the guards couldn't see.

At last, Daedalus had enough feathers. Next, he asked me to fetch some bendy willow branches. Then he spread the branches and feathers on the floor. He said, 'I'm going to make wings, so Icarus and I can fly to freedom.'

'Wings, Master?' I said, my eyes round with wonder. 'That's impossible!'

'I am Daedalus, the great inventor!' he answered. 'Nothing is impossible for *me*!'

I helped Daedalus make the wings. Icarus was too lazy and proud. He leaned against a wall, sulking.

My master and I worked hard. We stuck feathers to the branches with candle wax. At last, the wings were ready.

I looked at the wings and thought, *I would love to fly like a bird.*

Daedalus said, 'Icarus, tomorrow you and I will escape!'

49

That night, my master and Icarus were asleep. I lay in bed, wide awake.

My heart was beating fast. I wondered, *Do I dare?*

But then I decided, *Amara, you'll never get another chance!*

I strapped the small wings on to my back and arms.

I climbed up to the window and I looked down.

The guards were asleep.

'Fly, Amara!' I whispered.

I flapped my arms. For a second, I panicked. Was I going to fall? But suddenly, I swooped into the air. I flew higher and higher among the stars! I zoomed over the town, with a big grin on my face.

I shouted out, 'Flying is wonderful!'

But already the sun was rising. I knew I couldn't stay out any longer. Sadly, I landed back in the tower. I took off my beautiful wings and crept into bed.

Daedalus and Icarus strapped on the wings. Icarus boasted, 'We are the first people to fly!'

I smiled to myself. They didn't know my secret.

'Promise me, Icarus,' said my master. 'Don't fly too near the sun—or the wax on your wings will melt.'

'Don't fuss, Father!' snapped Icarus.

They stood in the window looking scared but excited. Then they took off!

They flew over the sea. I thought,
They really are going to escape!

But Icarus forgot his father's warning.
He soared higher and higher into the blue
sky, doing tricks and loop-the-loops. He
was having fun flying. I knew that feeling.
But he was too close to the sun!

I yelled from the
window, 'Be careful,
Icarus!' But he was
too far away to hear.

White feathers fell from Icarus's wings like snow. I watched in horror. His wings were breaking into pieces! Icarus fell like a stone through the air. He fell into the sea and didn't come up again.

Poor Icarus had drowned.

Daedalus couldn't help his son now. He wept as he flew to freedom.

But Icarus will never be forgotten. To this very day, we call the sea where he fell the Icarian Sea. We will always remember the boy who flew too close to the sun.

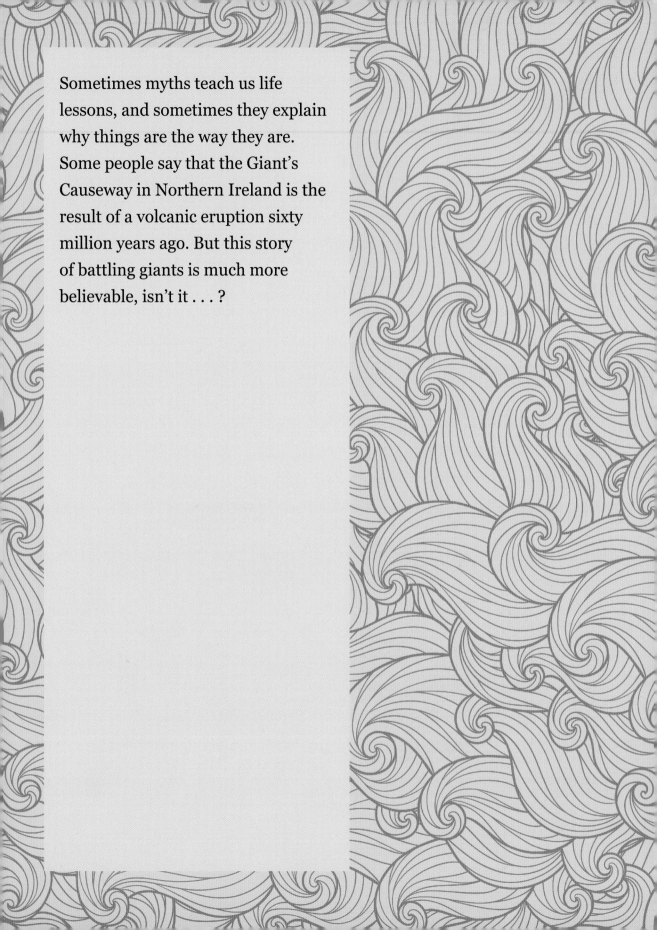

Sometimes myths teach us life lessons, and sometimes they explain why things are the way they are. Some people say that the Giant's Causeway in Northern Ireland is the result of a volcanic eruption sixty million years ago. But this story of battling giants is much more believable, isn't it . . . ?

Finn MacCool
and the Giant's Causeway

Retold by John Dougherty

Illustrated by Lee Cosgrove

Long, long ago, there lived in Ireland a mighty giant by the name of Finn MacCool. Finn was taller than an oak tree and stronger than a dozen oxen. He was brave and kind, but he was also very proud.

'I am the greatest giant of them all!' he would boast. 'There is no one who can beat me!'

Across the sea in Scotland, there lived another giant. This one was called Angus. He was huge and strong, with an angry red face, and everyone feared him.

One day, Angus was told of Finn's boasting. When he heard that Finn thought he was the greatest giant of all, Angus flew into a rage.

'I am the greatest giant!' he roared. 'I'll teach Finn a
lesson he won't forget!'

Angus strode angrily to the shore. He looked across at
Ireland. Cupping his hands to his mouth, he bellowed, 'Hey!
Finn MacCool! Come and see what a *real* giant looks like,
you great baby!'

The breeze carried his words to Finn and when Finn heard them, his temper rose. Standing on the cliffs of County Antrim, he roared back, 'All I see is a giant fool!'

At this, Angus shook with anger. 'If I could only get across the sea to you . . . !' he shouted. 'I would teach you a lesson you'd never forget!'

'That's easily done!' Finn replied. He tore a great rock from the cliffs and hurled it into the waves—the first stone of a giant pathway across the sea.

Angus began to do the same, but as the giants drew closer to one another Finn began to worry. He was getting tired, and Angus did look very big, and very strong.

So Finn hurried home to his wife, Oona. She was not as big or as strong as he was, but she was very clever. He told her all about Angus, and the path across the sea.

Oona sighed. 'Finn,' she said, 'you're being a big baby.'

'I am not being a baby!' Finn said.

Oona put a baby's bonnet on his head. 'You are now,'

she told him, and she gave him a nightgown and
made their bathtub look like a giant cot. 'Lie
down,' she told Finn, 'and leave Angus to me.'

Soon there came a loud knock on the door. Oona

opened it. There stood Angus, his
face redder and angrier than ever.

'I've come to see Finn,' he growled.

Oona smiled. 'Come in,' she said.
'He's out hunting, but he'll be
back soon.'

'Are you a friend of Finn's?' Oona asked.

'No,' snarled Angus. 'I've come to show him that I'm stronger than he is.'

'Really?' said Oona. 'A little fellow like you?'

'Little?' said Angus crossly. 'I'm the biggest giant there is!'

Oona smiled. 'I don't mean to be rude,' she said, 'but you're hardly bigger than Finn's baby.' And she nodded at the cot where Finn lay staring up with wide, nervous eyes.

'Goo, goo,' said Finn.

Angus looked at the cot. 'My!' he said. 'What a big baby!'

'Not really,' Oona said. 'Not when you think how big his daddy is.'

Now Angus began to worry. If Finn's baby was so big,

Finn must be much bigger!

'Still,' he said, 'Finn may be big, but he can't be as strong as I am!'

'I'm glad to hear it,' said Oona. 'I have a job that needs

doing. If you're stronger than Finn is, you'll find it easy.'

'I'm sure I will,' said Angus.

'I'm glad to hear it,' Oona said. 'I'd like you to turn the house around.'

Angus stared. 'Turn the house around?' he said.

'Why, yes,' said Oona. 'Finn always turns the house around at this time of the day. I like the sun to shine in the door.'

Angus gulped. He went outside and took hold of the house.

Then he heaved, and heaved, and heaved . . .

. . . and, very slowly, he turned the house around.

In his cot, Finn felt the house move. He put his thumb in his mouth and sucked it, worrying. Angus must be very strong to do such a thing.

At last, Angus finished turning the house.

'There!' he said proudly.

'Well done,' said Oona. 'Finn can do it much faster than that, mind you.'

Angus's face fell.

'But that wasn't bad for such a little fellow,' Oona went on. 'You must be tired now. Come in and have a snack.'

Angus went in and sat down. Oona gave him a cake. She had just made it, and it was still hot.

'Try this,' she said. 'Finn likes nothing better than one of these cakes after he's been working hard.'

'Thanks,' said Angus, and he took a big bite.

But Angus did not know that Oona had baked a stone inside the cake.

'Ow!!!' he yelled.

'What's wrong?' Oona asked.

'I broke my tooth on your cake!' Angus howled.

'Really?' said Oona. 'You must have
very soft teeth. Finn loves these cakes. So does
the baby,' she added. She gave a cake to Finn,
but she was careful to give him a cake without
a stone inside. Finn ate it in three big bites.

'More!' he said. 'Mammy! More!'

Angus stared.

'That baby must have very strong teeth!' he said.

Oona smiled. 'Not really,' she said. 'Not when you think how strong his daddy is. You can feel them if you like.'

So Angus put his hand in Finn's
mouth, to feel his teeth . . .

. . . and Finn bit as hard as he could. Angus
yelled with pain.

Just then, Oona said, 'I think I hear Finn coming home.'

Angus's red face turned pale. If Finn's baby was so strong,
Finn must be much stronger.

'Is that the time?' he said. 'I'm sorry, but I have to go.'

'Angus fight Daddy!' said Finn.

'Not today,' Angus said.

'Angus fight baby!' said Finn, and he jumped out of the cot.

This was too much for Angus. He turned and ran. 'Help!' he cried. 'There's a giant baby after me!'

He ran all the way back to Scotland, tearing up the
path so that neither Finn nor the giant baby could follow.

And Finn and his clever wife laughed and laughed, knowing that Angus would never again cross the sea to Ireland in search of the mighty Finn MacCool.

   If you ever go to County Antrim, you may see the few
rocks that Angus left behind. They are still called the
Giant's Causeway, and they are one of the wonders of
the world.

What collection of myths and legends would be complete without one of King Arthur's adventures? In this story, King Arthur and his men must battle a terrifying giant. Debate has gone on for hundreds of years about whether King Arthur really existed or not. Most of the details we know come from the legends spoken, and then written down, about him, so it's impossible to know what is fact and what is fiction. What makes you believe that a story is true?

The Giant of Mont Saint-Michel

Retold by Jeanne Willis

Illustrated by Nicolás Aznárez

n the island of Mont Saint-Michel, there lived a giant.

He had legs like tree trunks . . . fists like rocks . . . and a wicked heart.

The giant lived all alone, but he wanted to be like other men. So he went to find a wife.

His footsteps shook the earth:

BOOM! CRASH!

He crushed the villagers like ants.

He found Helena, who was the daughter of a duke.

He grabbed her in his huge fist.

'Wife!' he roared. The giant took Helena
back to his island.

Some knights sailed over the sea to save her. But the giant hit their boat with rocks and it sank.

The duke went to see King Arthur. 'Please save my daughter!' he begged.

So that night, the King and his men sailed to the island of Mont Saint-Michel.

King Arthur and his men marched into a dark wood.

In the wood they heard someone crying. It was an old woman. 'Go home!' she wailed. 'Go home or the giant will crush your bones.'

'I will kill the giant or die trying,' said Arthur. 'March on, men!'

The giant was waiting for
King Arthur and his men.

The King waved his sword and cut the
giant's forehead.

The giant picked up his club.

He swung it so hard, the wind blew
King Arthur off his feet.

'Oh no!' said his men. 'The King is no
match for the giant!'

Then the cut on the giant's forehead began to bleed. Blood went into his eyes so he could not see.

King Arthur thrust his sword into the giant's heart, and he fell.

BOOM!

CRASH!

King Arthur rescued Helena and took her back to the duke's castle. 'The giant is dead!' he said.

'Good always wins in the end,' said the duke. 'Long live Good King Arthur!'

97

The Lambton Worm is a legend from County Durham in north-east England. As with most myths, the details of the story change with each telling, but all revolve around John Lambton's battle with a giant worm. The Lambtons were a real family, and many of them died a violent death—perhaps the family really were cursed . . .

The
Lambton Worm

Retold by Jeanne Willis

Illustrated by Pierre Kleinhouse

Long ago, John Lambton went fishing on a Sunday. The villagers were shocked. 'Tut tut! Fishing?' they said. 'That boy should not be out having fun on a Sunday!'

John was the son of a lord. He thought he could do as he pleased. So he sat by the River Wear and fished.

After two hours, he had caught nothing. He was about to pack up and go.

Suddenly he felt a sharp tug on his line.

He had caught something! He tried
to pull it in, but it fought hard.
It must be a huge fish! thought John.

At last, he dragged it onto the bank. But it was not a fish.
It was a slimy black worm with an ugly head. It was small
but scary . . . and very smelly!

It wriggled and snapped at John. Its teeth
were as sharp as needles.
John did not like the look of it at all.

He was about to throw it back in the river. Just then, a
strange old man appeared.

'Keep it, or you will be sorry, lad!' said the old man.
Then he vanished into thin air.

There is something fishy going on, thought John.

He put the worm in his fishing basket.

But it looked so evil he was afraid to keep it.

So he threw it down the village well.

John went home to Lambton Hall.
'Did you catch any fish?' asked
Lord Lambton.
'No, Father,' said John.
He did not dare tell him
about the worm.

Years went by and nothing terrible happened. John grew up and went off to war. He forgot all about the worm.

But the worm did not forget about him. It was still in the well. It grew and grew.

Soon, it had grown into a giant serpent.
One night, it slithered out of the well. It
went back to the river and wrapped itself around
the island.

The next day the worm made its way to Lambton Hall.

'Let's feed it before it kills us all!' said the villagers.

They gave it a trough of milk. The worm drank the lot and left. It wrapped itself around Penshaw Hill and slept.

But every day, the worm came back. It wanted more.
The villagers fed it milk and cows and sheep. They
knew it would kill them if they did not.

Every night, it went back to Penshaw Hill to sleep.
The villagers lived in fear.

After seven years, John came back from war.
On his way home, he met a wise woman.
 'John Lambton, you put the worm in the well,'
she said. 'So you are the only one who can kill it.'
 John went pale. How did she know his secret?

'How can I kill the worm?' he asked.

'Tell the blacksmith to make you a suit of spiky armour,' she said. 'When the worm wraps itself around you, the spikes will stab it.'

'I will go to the blacksmith now,' said John.

'Wait!' said the wise woman. 'There is more! After you kill the worm, return to Lambton Hall. You must kill the first thing you see when you arrive. If you do not, the Lambton family will have nothing but bad luck.'

When the armour was ready, John put it on.

'Father, I am going to kill the worm,' he said.
'Afterwards, I will blow my horn and you must send
the dog to greet me.'

'Why?' asked Lord Lambton.

'I must kill the first thing I meet on my return.
If I don't, we will be cursed,' said John.

That night, he rode to Penshaw Hill.

The worm was wrapped around it.

John crept up. Suddenly, it grabbed him!

It wrapped him in its giant coils.

John gasped for breath. The worm
squeezed him tighter and tighter.
But as it squeezed, the spikes
on the armour stabbed it.

STAB!
STAB!
STAB!

At last, the worm
was dead!

John rode back to Lambton Hall and blew his horn. But the dog did not run out to greet him.

Instead Lord Lambton rushed to greet his son. John could not kill his father!

Just then, the dog ran out too and John killed it instead.

Alas, he had not done as the wise woman said.

After that, the Lambtons had nothing but bad luck. Everyone said that they were cursed.

And all because John Lambton went fishing on a Sunday!

Have you ever wished that you could live in the woods, learn how to shoot a bow and arrow, steal from the rich and give to the poor? What job do you think you would have if you were in Robin Hood's band of Merry Men? You'll have to think of what you're good at, just like Allan the minstrel!

The Legend of Robin Hood

Retold by Michaela Morgan

Illustrated by Mark Beech

Robin was running, running, running for his life. Behind him a gang of burly men shouted.

Robin glanced back. The soldiers were getting closer! They were going to catch him.

But Robin was a quick thinker. He saw a clump of bushes and quick as a wink he leapt into it. He lay safely hidden in the leafy damp as the soldiers pounded by.

Robin lay still as a stone,

breathing as quietly as he could.
'Safe at last!' he thought.

It was then he saw that the leaves and
bushes all around him were moving . . . they
were moving towards him!

Were the trees really coming to life? No! It was a group of shabby men. They were muddy and dirty. Some of them had leaves and twigs in their clothes and hair.

'Who are you?' they asked.

'I am Robin of Loxley Hall but . . .' Robin's voice shook.
'The Sheriff took my home and now my family are all . . .'

'We understand, lad,' said one of the men.

'We've lost our families and homes too. Now we live
like wild animals in these woods. The Sheriff's men call
us outlaws and try to hunt us down—but they can't
find us in here. You can join us. You'll be safe from the
soldiers in the woods.'

The next morning Robin woke up. It hadn't been easy
to get to sleep on the cold, hard ground.

During the night it had rained. Robin and all the outlaws
were wet, freezing, and very, very, VERY hungry.

127

Robin had an idea. He had one *great* skill
that could help these men.
He took his bow and
arrow and went
off hunting . . .

. . . and soon he
was back with plenty of meat.
'Build a big fire,' he laughed. 'Let's get cooking!'

Soon, the men were warm, well fed, and happy. One of the band spoke up. 'I think Robin should be our leader.'

The others agreed. Robin grinned. He had found a new home and family.

As the days passed, Robin organized the men.

Winter was coming so they built huts.

They camouflaged the huts with leaves and twigs.

Inside, they used heaps of leaves to make soft beds.

Robin made a new outfit for himself. It had a hood of green that he could pull over his head when he needed to hide among the bushes.

He gave himself a new name.

'I am no longer Robin of Loxley,' he said. 'From now on, I am Robin Hood.'

Let the adventures begin!

Robin trained the band.

He taught them how to make a bow and arrow.

He taught them how to *use* a bow and arrow.

They learnt how to climb and move quickly through the forest.

They learnt how to find their own food.

But most importantly, Robin taught them
to help the poor and people in need.

As the days went by, Robin saw that some of the men were becoming good archers.

And some were not!

Robin made a decision.

I'll give each of you a special job to suit your talents!

So, some became archers.

Some became lookouts.

Some became cooks.

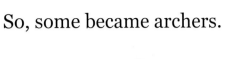

Some became hunters.

Some built the huts.

135

And then there was Allan . . .
Allan did not
like fighting.

He was a terrible cook.

And the huts he built . . .

. . . fell down.

'What are you good at?' Robin asked him.

'I am good at telling stories and making music. Oh, and I'm good at singing songs!' said Allan.

'Then you shall be our minstrel!' said Robin.

Allan told tales to keep the men cheerful. He sang songs all about Robin Hood and his Merry Men. He sang his songs wherever he went—in market squares, at festivals, and at fairs.

Soon, everyone had heard about Robin Hood. More and more people came to join his band. They all wanted to help the poor and to fight the wicked Sheriff and his soldiers.

One night, Robin was on lookout when he saw a boy
coming through the woods. Robin jumped out. Immediately
the boy pulled out his sword and started
to fight.

It was a fierce fight but a fast one. Robin was an expert
with a sword and much bigger than the boy.

When he had won, Robin stepped out of the shadows
and into the moonlight.

'You fight bravely,' said Robin. 'Would you like to join us and
fight the wicked Sheriff?'

Then, to Robin's surprise, the boy burst into tears.

'I thought *you* were one of the Sheriff's men,' the boy sobbed. Then Robin saw that he had made a mistake. It wasn't a boy. It was a girl!

'My name is Marion,' said the girl. 'The Sheriff and his men have taken my home. He locked my parents up. He locked me up too but I took these clothes and ran away to get help. He wants me to marry one of his men.'

Robin called for his band of men and they set off to rescue Marion's home and family.

When they arrived at Marion's castle it was still dark.

'I'll show you a secret way in,' she whispered.

She led them in and put on a dress. 'They will be coming for me soon,' she said. 'It's almost daylight.'

Morning came and in marched the Sheriff.

'Well Marion, I hope a long night alone in the dark has helped you learn your lesson. It's time for you to marry my fine friend! You can't fight us.'

'Yes I can!' shouted Marion.

'You and whose army?' mocked the Sheriff.

'This army!' said Marion as one by one the Merry Men appeared.

They came from behind the curtains . . .

from under the bed . . .

from out of the shadows.

One by one they
stepped out and drew
their swords.

The Sheriff took one look and turned and ran down the stairs, out of the castle, and across the fields. Robin's men chased him.

'Catch him! Cut off his ears!' shouted Robin. But he was joking. He just wanted the Sheriff to know what it was like to be chased and frightened.

Marion hugged and kissed her parents. '*My* family and home are safe now!' she smiled. But other people needed help too.

She looked at Robin. 'Let me join the band.'

'Well . . .' said Robin. 'You are brave. You can use a sword . . .

and you can use your head, so I say . . .

. . . yes, you can join us!'

Everyone cheered. Allan sang a song.

*Our band is made of merry men
And merry maids as well,
We fight for good with Robin Hood
And have fine tales to tell!
We help the poor and needy,
We fight the bullies and the greedy,
We'll fight for good with Robin Hood
And have fine tales to tell!*

Thor is the Norse god of thunder, and is the protector of mankind. He is incredibly strong, but sometimes you need more than physical strength to solve a problem. In lots of the Norse myths, Loki, the Master of Mischief, causes trouble for the rest of the gods, but in this story his cunning and cleverness might actually be quite useful. Would you trust him?

Thor and the Stolen Hammer

Retold by Tony Bradman

Illustrated by Glen McBeth

It was morning in Asgard, home of the Norse gods. One of the gods was very cross.

Thor was stomping around outside the main hall, chucking thunderbolts—CRASH! BANG! BOOM! He was doing a lot of shouting and yelling, too.

'What's wrong with old Thor today?' said Freya with a wince. She was the most beautiful goddess of them all. 'He sounds like a bear with a sore head.'

'Er . . . I think we're about to find out,' said Odin, greatest of the gods. He pushed his breakfast bowl to one side and gave a deep sigh. 'Here he comes . . .'

The door flew open and Thor marched in. His face
was red with anger.

'My wonderful hammer has gone!'
he roared. 'Did either of you take it?'

'Well, don't look at me,' Freya said snootily.
'Who cares about your stupid hammer, anyway?
I only hope you'll be quieter without it.'

'Actually, Freya, we should all care
about Thor's hammer,' said Odin. He looked
worried. 'Thor needs it to protect Asgard against
the ice giants . . .'

The gods of Asgard had been fighting the ice
giants since the beginning of time. Thor was the
one god the ice giants truly feared. That
was because he used his hammer to crack
their icy skulls.

'Ah—I hadn't thought of that,' said Freya.
'This could mean trouble . . .'

'Trouble? I like the sound of that,' said a voice.
Another god popped his head round the door.
He grinned cheekily. It was Loki, known as The
Master of Mischief.

Odin tutted and ignored him.

'Perhaps you've just forgotten where you put it, Thor,' Odin said. 'You know what you're like. You can be very forgetful.'

'Not where my hammer is concerned,' growled Thor. 'I always leave it in the corner of my room when I go to bed at night. And it wasn't there this morning!'

'Umm, how strange . . .' murmured Loki, with a puzzled

look on his face. Then he smiled. 'Can I borrow your marvellous coat of feathers, dear Freya?'

'Be my guest,' said Freya, shrugging. 'Just make sure you don't get it dirty.'

Loki pulled on the magic coat of falcon feathers and flew off.

Moments later, Loki was back.

'Just as I thought,' he said. 'Thrumir, the chief of the giants, sneaked in and stole your hammer, Thor. He says he won't give it back unless Freya marries him.'

'Definitely not!' said Freya. 'I won't marry a giant! They are all so *ugly* and *common*.'

'Don't worry, you won't have to,' snarled Thor, his face grim.

He clenched his fists and his huge muscles bulged. 'Just wait till I get my hands on him!'

'But what if he's hidden your hammer?' said Loki. 'We need to find out where he's put it. Listen, I've got a much better idea. Let's give him Freya—only it will be you in disguise, Thor . . .'

161

Thor realized what disguise they were planning.

'Oh no, I'm not getting dressed up as a . . . woman!' he spluttered, horrified.

Odin and Freya grinned at each other. 'Oh yes you are!' they said, and got to work.

Thor soon stood awkwardly before them. He wore one of Freya's dresses and a blonde wig with plaits. He wore her best necklace too, and Loki held a veil, ready to cover his rugged face.

'Perfect!' said Odin. 'The colour of that dress really suits you, Thor.'

'Oh, thanks . . .' said Thor, then scowled as Odin and
Freya burst into laughter. 'Very funny, I don't think,' Thor
grumbled. 'Can we get on with it, Loki?'

A little while later Loki and Thor arrived at the castle of the ice giants.

Loki had already sent a message to tell
Thrumir that his lovely bride
was on her way.

'You'd better let me do the talking, Thor,' Loki
whispered as they went through the gates. Thor nodded.

The two gods were led to the dining hall.

'Welcome, Freya!' said Thrumir. He was huge and ugly and the hall was packed full of giants just like him. 'I can't tell you how happy I am . . .'

'Er . . . Freya feels just the same,' said Loki. 'I see you've laid on a feast.'

168

'Yes, and I'd like Freya to sit beside me,' said Thrumir with a big smile.

Loki nudged Thor, and the god of thunder stomped off to do what he was told. Loki sat down too, and the feast began.

Thor liked his food. He gobbled up everything in sight.

He ate three roast chickens,

five legs of lamb,

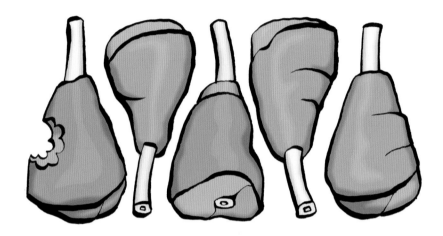

and eight salmon.

Then, he leant back and gave a loud . . .

BURP!

Loki glared at Thor, but Thrumir seemed impressed. 'What a wonderful woman you are,' he said. 'Could I just, er . . . lift your veil a little?'

'Not till you give us Thor's hammer,' said Loki. 'That was the deal.'

171

Thrumir clicked his giant fingers.
The hammer was brought out.

'Happy now?' said Thrumir. 'Come
on, Freya, how about a kiss?'

'You must be joking!' growled Thor.
He pulled off his veil and grabbed
his hammer.

Thrumir stared at him with his mouth open—but soon closed it when Thor brought his hammer down on the giant's skull with a loud . . . **CRACK!**

Thor did the same to every giant in the hall—
CRACK! CRACK! CRACK!
Then he chucked some thunderbolts just for fun—
CRASH! BANG! BOOM!

'Well, that's sorted them out,' said Loki, looking around at the smoking ruins of Thrumir's castle. 'Maybe you should dress up as a woman more often, Thor.'

'I don't think so,' said Thor. 'Poor old Freya couldn't stand the competition.' Then he roared with laughter and Loki grinned.

The two friends headed back to Asgard, feeling very pleased with themselves. Thor had his beloved hammer again and Loki had outwitted the ice giants. And they both knew they had a great story that would be told and retold for a very long time.

Vulcan is the Roman god of fire and volcanoes. There is a god of fire and volcanoes in Greek mythology too, called Hephaestus. Isn't it amazing that even though the Ancient Greeks lived about 1,000 years before the Ancient Romans, their myths continued to be passed down through the centuries, making their mark on future civilizations.

Vulcan and the Fabulous Throne

Retold by Tony Bradman

Illustrated by Andrés Martínez Ricci

It should have been a happy time on Mount Olympus, home of the gods. Juno, wife of Jupiter, the king of the gods, had just had a baby.

But Juno had taken one look at the little red-faced creature . . . and screamed.

'Try to stay calm, my love,' Jupiter said. 'I know you're disappointed . . .'

'Disappointed?' squealed Juno. 'That's putting it mildly. I mean, we are the most beautiful beings in the universe. So how come our baby is so . . . ugly?'

'It's a puzzle, isn't it?' said Jupiter, frowning. Then he smiled. 'Still, we'll have to make the best of it, sweetheart. Er . . . perhaps his looks will improve.'

'Well, I'm not waiting to find out!' said Juno. 'This baby will have to go!'

'Hold on a moment . . .' said Jupiter. 'Now, don't do anything silly . . .'

But before Jupiter could stop her, Juno picked up the baby and threw him high into the sky.

The baby whizzed over the woods and mountains
and villages, then dropped towards the island of Sicily.

He flew through the smoke and flames belching out
of Mount Etna, the island's great volcano.

Then he plunged into the sparkling blue waters of the sea with a huge **SPLASH!**

And that's when the baby's luck changed . . .

He was found on the beach by Thetis, a sea nymph with a kind heart.

'You poor little thing!' she said. 'I'll take you home and look after you!'

He needed quite a lot of looking after. He was covered in black ash from Mount Etna, and had broken a leg when he'd fallen into the sea.

Thetis named him Vulcan.

The years went by, and Vulcan grew into a strong, sturdy boy. His broken leg healed but he was left with a slight limp. Vulcan was quiet and shy, but he loved Thetis and she loved him. They lived happily in their cave by the sea.

Then Vulcan discovered that he also loved playing with fire . . .

One day the volcano rumbled and grumbled and threw out some fiery rock. Vulcan found it. He was fascinated by the way it glowed and gave off heat.

'Look at this, Thetis,' he said. 'Isn't it amazing? What can I do with it?'

'Well, you could set fire to my dress if you're not more careful!' said Thetis nervously. 'Why don't you pretend that you're a blacksmith? I'll help you.'

Thetis set up a little forge for him on the beach, and Vulcan spent the rest of that day lost in a brilliant game. At least that's what Thetis thought at first. But it soon became clear that young Vulcan was taking it all very seriously.

'I've made a few bits and pieces, Thetis,' he said shyly one afternoon.

'So I see . . .' said Thetis, her eyes wide with surprise. 'That's wonderful!'

A great heap of metal objects stood next to Vulcan's forge—horse shoes,

wheel rims and shovels,

swords and spears and shields.
Vulcan was a natural
blacksmith.

He loved making things for Thetis as well. One day he made her a beautiful gold necklace to wear to a party with the other sea nymphs. Everybody asked Thetis who had made it. Thetis told them, but that was a BIG mistake . . .

187

Juno heard about the amazing necklace—and decided she wanted one too.

'In fact, I want the person who made it to come and live here on Mount Olympus,' she said. 'Then he can make me lots and lots of lovely jewellery.'

'Er . . . you do realize that person is our baby, don't you, dear?' said Jupiter. 'You know, the ugly one that you didn't want to keep and threw away.'

'Is that so?' said Juno. 'Well, he can't say no to his own mother, can he?'

189

But Vulcan did say no. He refused point-blank to do what Juno wanted.

'Why should I?' he said to Thetis. 'She was horrible to me when I was a baby, and besides, I like living here with you. You're my real mum, not her.'

'What a sweet boy you are,' said Thetis and kissed him. 'But I still think we have to do something. It's not a good idea to upset the Queen of Olympus.'

'No problem,' said Vulcan with a crafty smile. 'I've got just the thing . . .'

Later that day a special delivery arrived on Mount Olympus.
It was a gift for Juno from Vulcan. Juno gasped as she
unwrapped a fabulous golden throne studded with jewels.
'Wow, not bad!' said Juno, smiling.

But the instant she sat on it, steel bands snapped round her ankles and wrists. 'Help!' she screamed. 'I'm trapped!'

Jupiter tried to free her. All the other gods tried too, but it was no use.

'I'm sorry, my dear,' said Jupiter. 'I think you're well and truly stuck.'

'Oh no!' said Juno, and burst into tears. 'I'm sure this is a punishment for what I did to that poor baby. You know, I've been feeling guilty ever since . . .'

'Have you really?' said Jupiter, surprised. 'Well, I did warn you. Hang on a second though, what's this? There's some writing on the back of the throne.'

Jupiter read it out. 'One little word will free you—and all will be forgiven.'

Juno looked at him, puzzled for a moment. But then she smiled, and said the magic word. 'Sorry . . .'

The steel bands snapped open, and Juno was free.

Happy times returned to Mount Olympus. Vulcan came to visit his parents and they became good friends. Jupiter built a great forge for Vulcan deep in the heart of Mount Etna. And Vulcan made fiery thunderbolts for his father to throw.

But his home was always with Thetis, in their cave by the sparkling sea.

Sometimes it's tricky to pronounce the names in myths. Here's some help:

Hercules (**her**-cue-leez)
Eurystheus (yoo-**ris**-thee-us)
Iolaus (eye-oh-**lay**-us)
Augeas (**aw**-jee-us)
Cretan (**kree**-tonne)
Diomedes (dye-uh-**mee**-deez)
Hippolyte (hi-**pol**-i-tuh)
Geryon (**geh**-ree-un)
Hades (**hay**-deez)
Styx (**sticks**)
Cerberus (**sir**-ber-us)

Hercules
the Hero

Retold by Michaela Morgan

Illustrated by Glen McBeth

Long, long ago in Greece, the gods lived high in the sky. The ordinary little humans lived down on the ground. But in between gods and humans there was another race.

We call them . . . the heroes.

Have a look at them.

Jason

Atlanta

Perseus

Heroes were half god, half human. They were larger than life, stronger than strong, braver than brave. They were born to battle beasts and mangle monsters.

All the heroes had special powers. The biggest hero of them all was Hercules.

When Hercules was just an itty bitty baby, an enemy sneaked along and put two snakes in his cot. These were deadly snakes with fierce fangs full of venom.

What did baby Hercules do?

He picked them up, one in each hand and . . .

. . . rattled them.

As the years went by, Hercules grew stronger . . .

and **stronger** . . .

and **stronger**.

But Hercules was half human and he had a lot to learn.
The gods looked down and spoke about him.

He needs tests!

He needs quests!

A good job will help him settle down!

Then the gods spoke to Hercules:

You have lessons to learn. You must go to work for King Eurystheus. If you do everything you are told you will pass our tests.

King Eurystheus was a nasty man . . . and he hated Hercules.

He decided to give Hercules twelve impossible tasks.

The King smiled a false smile and turned to Hercules. 'Your first task is to kill the Giant Lion,' he said.

No one could kill the Giant Lion. It had a very special skin. Arrows just bounced off it. Knives just buckled.

Other hunters had tried to fight the lion. They had never been seen again.

They had all been pounced on . . . and eaten.

'Hee hee,' sniggered King Eurystheus. 'That's the end of Hercules the Hulk!'

Hercules tracked the lion, took careful aim, and fired his arrows.

Ping they went as they bounced off.

So Hercules threw stones. *Clunk* they went as they bounced off. He threw rocks. He threw boulders. He threw trees. KERRRRRASH! Nothing worked. Luckily, Hercules could run like the wind!

Then Hercules tried using his brain.

Hercules was clever. He waited until nightfall. Then he sneaked into the entrance of the lion's cave and he blocked the exit.

The lion could not run now and had no room to pounce. All he could do was wrestle. And Hercules was a star wrestler.

'Haroooo!' cried Hercules and he wrestled the lion to the ground.

Using only his mighty hands, Hercules overpowered the Giant Lion.

Hercules took the lion's skin and wore it as a cloak.

He wore the lion's gaping jaws as a helmet.

This is what he looked like:

Now Hercules was a superhero with a super costume that no arrows, knives—or teeth could get through to harm him. Result!

When King Eurystheus saw Hercules clad in the lion's skin thundering back down the road, he was terrified.

The quivering King ran and hid in a big storage jar. From inside this jar King Eurystheus gave his next order.

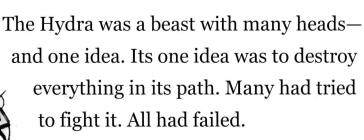

The Hydra was a beast with many heads—and one idea. Its one idea was to destroy everything in its path. Many had tried to fight it. All had failed.

Imagine this awful beast rising before you, rearing its many heads. All the heads have razor teeth, blazing eyes . . . and the foulest breath.

The Hydra's breath was so foul it was lethal. One whiff—and you were dead.

And its feet! They were even worse! Even smelling the *footprints* of this foul beast would kill an ordinary man.

Luckily, Hercules was no ordinary man.

He set off and took his young nephew Iolaus with him.

Bravely they made their way into the swamp where the creature lurked. The stench was vile.

Hercules drew his sword and the fight began.

With a swish of his sword Hercules cut off one of the Hydra's heads. But before he had time to cheer and say 'Yesssssss!' two more heads had grown back in its place!

Swish, Swish. Hercules chopped off two more heads. Immediately, four more heads grew back.

Hercules was good at sums. He worked out that he couldn't win like this.

Just when Hercules had decided it couldn't get any worse . . . it got worse.

A giant crab grabbed hold of the hero's leg.

Iolaus was a quick thinker. He swung his burning torch to frighten off the crab.

Then each time Hercules chopped off a Hydra head, Iolaus seared the wounded stump. With a sizzle he stopped another head from growing.

The Hydra was defeated.

'I couldn't have done it without you, boy,' said Hercules as they set off back to King Eurystheus.

The second task was done.

King Eurystheus was so scared of Hercules now that he stayed in his jar.

His voice echoed inside it.

Bring me the deer that belongs to the goddess Diana!

Now this deer was very special. It was a favourite of the hunting goddess. Its antlers were made of pure gold. It was fleet of foot . . . and it was very hard to find.

For one whole year Hercules hunted the deer. Finally, one day he caught a glimpse of it. He did not want to kill or harm the deer.

So he took VERY careful aim and just pinned it down without drawing blood.

Proudly, Hercules led the golden animal back to King Eurystheus.

Was the King pleased?

He was not.

He immediately sent Hercules off to find another fierce creature—a giant wild boar. But in next to no time, Hercules came stomping back with the wild boar carelessly slung over his shoulders.

King Eurystheus was filled with anger. This time he thought up a truly terrible task.

'You must clean the stables of King Augeas,' said the King.

Now *you* may have to tidy your room sometimes. That might seem like hard work—but this was MUCH worse.

King Augeas had a massive stable and in it he kept a huge number of animals. He had hundreds upon hundreds of horses, thousands and thousands of cows, millions of chickens . . .

. . . and sheep and goats.

He had kept animals for countless years and he had NEVER, **EVER** cleaned up after them.

Vast heaps of dung had piled up over the years.

Hercules held his nose. And shook his head.

This was a real stinker of a job.

Did Hercules have an enormous bucket and a gigantic spade?
He did not.

But he did have heroic strength. He also had imagination.
So this is what he did . . .

He rolled up part of the earth and joined two rivers
together and washed the stables clean! He didn't even get
his hands dirty!

Was that enough for King Eurystheus? No! He wanted more.

He asked Hercules to hunt down some birds. These were not little fluffy tweety birds.

Oh no! These birds had beaks of bronze and claws of copper—and jaws that could crush a man. And that's what they did. They swarmed in the swamps and they feasted on flesh.

Hercules took his nephew along for the adventure. Together they tracked these cruel birds down to their swamp. But every time Hercules put a foot on the swampy ground the ground tried to swallow him up. The birds hid in the trees, safely out of reach.

'We could shoot them easily if they would take off and fly,' muttered Iolaus—and that's when he had a brilliant idea.

Iolaus played loud music. He danced a crazy dance. He stamped and stomped and whooped. The birds took flight. Then the hero and his nephew loosed their arrows. Job done!

For his next adventure, Hercules had to catch the Cretan bull. Catching a bull is bad enough but this was a burping bull—and he belched flames.

Hercules wrestled the bull to the ground. The lion skin protected Hercules from the flames.

King Eurystheus immediately sent Hercules off again. This time the task was to capture the Mares of Diomedes.

'What are they?' asked Hercules.

'Horses,' the King replied.

'With many heads?' asked Hercules.

'No,' said Eurystheus.

'Do they belch flames?'

'No.'

'Do they have razor claws?'

'No.'

Easy peasy! thought Hercules and off he went.

King Diomedes welcomed him.

That's when Hercules found out what those horses ate . . .

The Mares of Diomedes dined on flesh.

Please stay for dinner!

Hercules fought with the King. In the end it was Diomedes that became the dinner.

Diomedes was such a bitter, tough old king that the mares lost their taste for flesh. They became vegetarians and became quite calm. Hercules led them back to King Eurystheus.

For his ninth task, Hercules was sent to the land of the Amazons to get a belt from a queen.

But this was no ordinary belt. This was no ordinary queen.

Hippolyte was Queen of the Amazons.

The Amazons were all women and all skilled warriors. They were archers and fine fighters.

Hippolyte listened to Hercules and agreed to give him the belt.

It was all going so well . . . and then an enemy started a rumour.

'Hercules is going to kidnap the Queen . . .'

Fierce fighting broke out and Hercules escaped by a whisker!

It wasn't long before King Eurystheus sent Hercules off to find something else. This time the King wanted cattle. But of course these were no ordinary cows. They belonged to Geryon.

Geryon was a monster with three heads and three sets of legs. He also had a fierce dog, which guarded the cattle. This dog only had two heads but each head had a set of razor teeth.

The dog leapt at Hercules. His razor teeth gleamed in the sun. Drools of saliva slobbered from his hungry mouth.

But Hercules had no fear of such creatures now. With a biff of his club Hercules sorted that guard doggy out. Then he rounded the cattle up and off he went.

For his eleventh test, Hercules was sent to get an apple.

Of course, he wasn't just sent to get an apple from the local supermarket. Oh no, these apples were grown in a magical grove, protected by magical girls—and a dragon. But help was at hand.

'I can get those apples for you,' boomed a voice. 'My name is Atlas. I hear you are a strong man, Hercules.'

'I am the strongest man on earth!' Hercules boasted.

'Then you can hold my burden,' said Atlas. 'Just hold it for a minute while I get the apples.'

Hercules agreed.

Ooof! What a weight was put on his shoulders! It was the weight of the world.

The gods had given Atlas the task of holding up the world.

Atlas thundered off and soon he was back with the apples.

'I feel so light without all that weight!' grinned Atlas. 'And you are doing such a super job. I'll see you later. Cheerio!'

'But that's not our deal!' Hercules complained.

'That's not fair!'

Atlas didn't care. He was too busy stretching and skipping and leaping and twirling.

'I feel as light as air!' he sang.

Hercules knew that he was not as big and strong as Atlas—but he was *clever*.

'Before you skip off,' said Hercules, 'can you get me a pillow for my shoulder?'

'All right,' said Atlas. 'You can use the one I had.'

'Will you just lift the world up and pop the pillow on my shoulders?' asked Hercules.

Atlas took the weight of the world and in that split second Hercules slipped out and left the world back on Atlas's shoulders.

'Sorry!' said Hercules. 'But we all have our tasks and *that* job was given to you.'

For the last task, King Eurystheus sent Hercules to the Land of the Dead, to battle with the Hound of Hell.

That's the last we'll see of him! **NO ONE** comes back from there!

Hercules travelled to the ends of the earth . . . and beyond.

Finally he came to Hades, the hellish land of the dead. It lay beyond a wide and chilly river—the River Styx. It was too wide and deep for Hercules to cross.
But there was a boat and a boatman.

'Will you ferry me across, please?' Hercules asked.

The boatman turned to face him. He wore a grey hooded robe. His face was invisible but his voice croaked, 'No! Not unless you pay me with your life.'

Hercules had travelled far and learnt much. He would not be stopped now. He glowered so fiercely that the bully boatman gave in. Then slowly, slowly the boatman ferried Hercules across to the Land of the Dead.

It was dark. Very dark. And yet at the same time there were shadows. Grey shadows writhed and whirled in the air. And there were sounds. Shrill screams. Distant howls. And a sort of hissing.

Hercules peered through the gloom . . .

. . . three pairs of evil yellow eyes glowered back at him. It was Cerberus, the three-headed Hound of Hell.

On each head there were swarms of lashing serpents. In each mouth, there were rows of teeth, glinting like knives.

GRRRRRRRRRRRRROWLLLLLLLL!

Cerberus pounced.

But Hercules was wearing the lion skin.

The serpents could not sting through it.

The deadly teeth could not rip through it.

Hercules wrestled the hound to the ground. He used all the force of his mighty hands.

He used everything he had learnt in his other adventures,

until . . .

. . . Cerberus, the Hound of Hell submitted.

Hercules had achieved the impossible.

He had fought the Hound of Hell.

He returned from the Land of the Dead.

The gods smiled on him.

From then on, Hercules lived a long and happy life.

At the end of his days he died a peaceful death.

He had earned his place in the Heavens so the gods gave him an honoured place with them on Mount Olympus.

Hercules
became a god.

I love this Arthurian tale—it's full of mystery and excitement and adventure. Every story in this collection has had thousands of tellers over the years, and *Gawain and the Green Knight* is no exception. This version was first written down in England the late fourteenth century, but legends about Gawain existed a few hundred years before that in English, Welsh, and Irish stories, and French ones too. I am adding my voice to those that have gone before; why don't you add yours too? Tell the story *your* way, let Gawain become your hero, and continue the renewal of the legend.

Gawain and the
Green Knight

Retold by Michael Morpurgo

Illustrated by Joanna Carey

It was cold at Christmas that year, and colder still at New Year, the snow thick on the ground. But neither the snow nor the wind could dampen the spirits of the Knights of the Round Table. Everyone was gathered at Camelot for the New Year's Eve feasting — the knights all in their places, King Arthur and Queen Guinevere sitting side by side. A blazing fire crackled in the hearth, the ale flowed freely, the harpist played as only he could play. The boar's head, an apple in its mouth, was carried into the hall, and the knights pounded the table impatiently.

At that moment, from outside in the courtyard, there came the clatter of a horse's hooves on the cobbles. The doors flew open, and a giant of a man rode in on a towering war horse that was pawing the ground, snorting its fury. The man swept the hall with terrible eyes, wolfish eyes that froze the courage in a man's veins. And he was green, green from head to foot. Green jerkin, common enough; green cloak, again, common enough; but his face was green, his hands as well. And his hair, which was long to his shoulders, was green too. The horse was green, and the saddle. This giant wore no armour, but carried a green axe in one hand.

King Arthur was the first to find his voice.

'Welcome, stranger,' he said. 'Why don't you come and join us?'

'I have not come here to waste my time in feasting. I can do that well enough at home. I have something else in mind. You are King Arthur?'

'I am.'

'Well, King Arthur,' he began, his voice heavy with sarcasm. 'The whole world talks of little but the so-called bravery of your knights. I have come all this way to find out just how brave you are. Looking about me, I see nothing but a bunch of beardless little boys. Are you quite sure I have come to the right place?'

At this, there were howls of protest. 'You may bark and howl loud enough,' he went on, 'but I doubt very much if there's anyone here man enough to accept my challenge. We shall see.' And he held out his axe in both hands. 'You see this axe? I will submit myself right now to one blow from this axe, just one blow—but only if, in twelve months and a day from now, I can repay the blow in kind, just one blow. There, is that simple enough for you dunderheads?'

No one moved a muscle. No one said a word.

'Well, I can see I was wrong,' laughed the green giant. 'I said I saw boys about me. I see only chickens.'

The King was on his feet. His blood was up. 'You've asked for it,' he shouted. 'I'll do it, and with pleasure too. Down off your horse.'

Then, suddenly, Sir Gawain was on his feet beside the King. 'No, sire,' he said. 'Let me. I'll soon shut his big mouth, once and for all.'

'Very well, Gawain,' the King replied, more than a little relieved.

With a great laugh, the Green Knight jumped down from his horse. 'So, Arthur, at least you have one man amongst all these boys,' he quipped.

'Enough!' cried Gawain, striding across the hall to meet him. Dwarfed, but not cowed, he squared up to the Green Knight. 'It will be a promise, a bargain between us,' he went on. 'I promise, on my honour as a knight, that I will strike you just once, as you've said; and that, in a year's time, you can do the same to me—if you're still able to, which I doubt.'

'We shall see,' said the Green Knight, and he handed Gawain his axe.

Gawain gripped the axe tightly. The Green Knight knelt down, pulling aside his long hair, so that his neck was bared. Gawain seemed to be hesitating for a moment.

'Come on then, Gawain, what are you waiting for? Are you frightened of the sight of a little blood? Strike man, strike!'

Gawain hesitated no longer. With one blow, he severed the Green Knight's head clean from his shoulders and sent it rolling across the floor. But there was not a drop of blood, green or red, not a single drop, and no time to wonder at it either, for the Green Knight sprang at once to his feet, picked up his head, and vaulted headless on to his horse. It was the severed head under the arm that spoke.

'You have a year and a day, Gawain. I am the Green Knight of the Green Chapel in the Forest of Wirral. You'll find me easily enough. If you do not, then the whole world will know that the great Sir Gawain is a coward and all King Arthur's court with him.' With that, he galloped away out into the snow, leaving the hall silent and aghast behind him.

The seasons passed as they always do, slowly enough for the young, but ever faster for the old. And for poor Gawain too, though still young in body and spirit, the year raced by and soon it was time for him to leave. He embraced the

King without a word, then mounted Gringolet, his black war horse, and rode off. No one thought he would ever return.

Gawain rode away with a heavy heart. He travelled up over the windswept hills of north Wales and down into the forests beyond. It was bitterly cold. Many a cold night he slept out in the open, and many a day passed with no food either for himself or his horse, so that they were both much weakened by the time they came at long last into the Forest of Wirral.

He asked anyone and everyone he met where he might find the Green Chapel, but no one seemed even to have heard of it.

He began to despair of ever finding the place in time. On and on he rode, ever deeper into the forest, wading through marsh and mud, until, on Christmas Eve, he found himself fording a stream and riding through open parkland towards a fine castle. The drawbridge over the moat was down, so he rode across and knocked at the door.

A porter greeted him with a welcoming smile and invited him to come in. Gringolet was led away for a rub-down, then to a warm, dry stable where there was all the sweet hay and all the clean water he could want. Gawain was brought into the hall to meet his host, the lord of the castle.

The moment Gawain set eyes on him, he knew he was in good hands, for everything about the man was courteous and kind, from his honest eyes to his open smile. Gawain told him at once who he was and where he had come from.

'No matter who you are,' said the lord of the castle, clasping his hand, 'you are more than welcome to my home. You need rest, and here you shall have all you require. My castle is your castle. Everything I have is yours for as long as you want to stay.' Gawain could hardly believe his good luck.

Then there began three days of Christmas celebrations. People flocked to the castle from miles around to meet

Gawain, and he was feted royally. Nothing was too much trouble. The lady of the castle, his host's wife, saw to his every need—and she was as beautiful a woman as Gawain had ever met. Never had he enjoyed a Christmas as much as this. But, from time to time, a shadow came over him as he thought of the dreaded appointment with the Green Knight, now only a few short days away. The happier he was, the less he wanted to die.

'You are sad, Gawain,' said the lady of the castle, as they sat talking together with the lord late one evening.

'After all you have done for me, my lady, I have no right to be,' Gawain replied. He had tried so hard to drive away his black and fearful thoughts. 'But I am afraid that tomorrow I shall have to leave and be on my way. I have promised to be at the Green Chapel on New Year's Day, and, as yet, I don't even know where the place is. I must not be late; I cannot be.'

'Nor shall you be,' laughed the lord of the castle, 'because the Green Chapel you speak of is no more than a two-hour ride from here, on a good horse. So why don't you stay here for three more days, until the morning of New Year's Day itself? I shall have someone show you the way, just to be sure. How would that be?'

Gawain was mightily relieved. 'That would make me the happiest man alive. You've been so good to me, so kind.'

'And since it's still the festive season,' his host said, 'why don't we play a little game? Let's make a bargain, you and I.'

'Why not?' Gawain said.

'I shall be going out hunting every day. What if I promise that I give you whatever I bring back from the hunt?' the lord of the castle went on. 'And you promise, in return, that you will give me anything and everything that comes your way back here in the castle? Well?'

'It's a bargain,' Gawain laughed. 'Anything at all that comes my way you shall have, I promise—though I can't for the life of me think what it might be.'

So early the next morning, the lord of the castle set out hunting while Gawain slept on. But as he dozed, the door of his room opened silently. Gawain opened his eyes to find the lady of the castle sitting on his bed smiling down at him. 'Will you kiss me, Gawain?' she asked.

'Well, if you're offering, my lady,' said Gawain, 'then who am I to turn you down?' And the lady leant over, took his face in her hands, and kissed him gently.

When she had gone, Gawain got up, washed and dressed, thinking all the while of the kiss. The whole day, he spent with the lady. She made him forget all his troubles, even his approaching encounter with the Green Knight in the Green Chapel.

At dusk, the lord of the castle returned, mud-splattered from the hunt. He strode into the hall and threw down a roe deer at Gawain's feet. 'Yours, as I promised,' he said. 'So. What have you got for me, then?'

'This,' said Gawain, and he took his host's face in his hands and kissed him. 'That's all. I promise.'

'I believe you,' laughed the lord of the castle, 'but what I'd like to know is how you came by this kiss.'

'Oh no,' said Gawain, shamefaced. 'That wasn't part of the bargain.' And they said no more about it. That night, the three of them feasted together happily, and talked and laughed into the early hours.

In the morning, Gawain woke to the sound of baying hounds and hunting horns. From his bed, he could see the lord of the castle riding out across the parkland. As he expected, and as he hoped too, it wasn't long before the lady came into his room. She sat on his bed, stroked his hair, and this time she offered him two kisses. Gawain did not find it at all difficult to accept.

That evening, the lord of the castle returned from the hunt, a boar slung across his shoulders. 'Here we are', he said. 'Not a bad day's work, eh? What about you?'

'Just this,' said Gawain. And, at that, he kissed him twice.

Gawain scarcely slept at all that night. Haunted by thoughts of his appointment with the Green Knight, he tossed and turned. It wasn't until dawn that he sank into a troubled sleep. When he woke, the lady of the castle was gazing down at him.

'As this is your last day here,' said the lady, 'I have a special gift for you.' And she handed him the belt she wore round her waist, a belt of green ribbon interwoven with gold thread. 'Wear it always, dear Gawain, and I promise you will never come to any harm, for there is within it an all-powerful magic. Wear it and you will be safe; wear it and think of me. One day, it may save your life.'

Gawain took the belt willingly. Tomorrow he had to face the Green Knight, and this belt could be the saving of him. Now he would at least stand some chance of survival. Now he had some hope of living beyond tomorrow.

'Dear, sweet Gawain,' whispered the lady, and she kissed him three times before leaving the room.

At sundown, Gawain was waiting in the hall when the lord of the castle came in from the hunt, swinging a fox by its brush. Gawain went right up to him, took him by the shoulders, and kissed him loudly three times. 'Three!' cried the lord of the castle, wiping his cheeks. 'And all I have to offer you in return is this pesky fox. Here, I wish you joy of it.'

Try as he might, Gawain could not enjoy the New Year's feast that night. There was wine, there was music, there was dancing. But hidden round his waist he could feel the lady's magic belt. He had not kept his promise to the lord of the castle; and, worse, he knew it was out of cowardice that he had broken the bargain. The belt might save his life the next day, but it would not save his honour. He had not kept to the agreement he had made with the lord. All night long, he lay in a turmoil of guilt, but he could not bring himself to hand

over the belt and give up his only chance of life.

Gawain was up early on New Year's Day. He tied the belt round his waist and put on his warmest clothes and his fine armour. Down in the courtyard, he embraced his host for the last time, unable to look him in the eye. He looked for the lady of the castle but she was nowhere to be seen. He mounted Gringolet and waved his farewells. They let down the drawbridge and, with a squire ahead to guide him, Gawain rode out into the biting January cold.

For nearly two hours they rode on, following a winding, tumbling stream along a mist-filled valley. Suddenly the squire reined in his horse and pointed. 'Over there,' he said, his voice hushed. 'Beyond those trees, you can't miss it—the Green Chapel.' The squire shuddered. 'Goodbye, Sir Gawain,' he said, and he rode away, leaving Gawain alone in the swirling mist.

Gringolet pawed the ground, eager to be going. 'Don't be in such a hurry,' said Gawain aloud. 'I just hope and pray the lady was telling the truth about this magic belt. If not—' And as he spoke, he heard from somewhere ahead of him a grating, grinding sound. He listened again. It was just as he feared, metal on stone. The Green Knight was sharpening his axe. Gawain shivered in spite of himself. 'What must be must be,' he sighed, and he put his spurs to Gringolet's sides, urging him onwards.

He rode through the dripping trees, crossed a stream, and came to a grassy mound. Near the mound stood a small chapel, the roof and walls as green as the surrounding grass. Gawain could hear the axe still being sharpened. He thought of galloping off and, but for the green belt, he would undoubtedly have done so. Instead he dismounted.

'Who's there?' he called out. 'I am Sir Gawain from King Arthur's court, and I have come as I promised I would. Come on out.'

'When my axe is sharp enough,' came the reply. 'I won't be long.' And the gruesome grinding ground on. Gawain waited, pacing up and down, until, at long last, out came the Green Knight. He was every bit as huge and as terrifying as Gawain had remembered. He looked mercilessly down at Gawain out of his green wolfish eyes. 'Welcome, Gawain,' he said.

'Let's not waste time,' said Gawain, longing now to have it done with. He felt his courage ebbing away with every passing moment.

'As you wish,' said the Green Knight. 'Take off your helmet.' Gawain removed his helmet, knelt down on the wet grass, and bent his head. He closed his eyes and waited, but nothing happened.

'Go on, then,' he said. He could speak in no more than a whisper. 'Go on. I won't move.'

The Green Knight whirled his great axe round his head, round and round, so that it whistled through the air. In spite of himself, Gawain could not stop himself from flinching.

'What's the matter with you, Gawain?' the Green Knight scoffed. I thought the knights of King Arthur's court were supposed to be so brave, and I heard Sir Gawain was the bravest of all.'

'Get on with it!' Gawain cried. 'All right, I winced; but I won't do it again.'

'We shall see,' laughed the Green Knight. Once again, he heaved up his axe. This time, he held back the blow to just a hair's breadth from Gawain's neck. Gawain felt the wind of it, but never moved a muscle.

'Well done, Gawain,' the Knight said. 'That was just to see how brave you really are. This time, though, there'll be no holding back. Prepare yourself.'

'Can you do nothing but talk?' Gawain was more angry than frightened now. 'Strike man, strike!'

A third time now, the Green Knight swung up his axe. And this time, the blade just nicked the skin on Gawain's neck. Gawain felt the pain of it and the warm blood trickling down. He was on his feet in an instant, springing back and drawing his sword.

'That's it!' he cried. 'You've had your chance. One stroke, just one stroke. That was the bargain. Now I can defend myself, and, by God, I will!'

But strangely, the Green Knight just smiled and threw aside his axe. 'No, Gawain.' He spoke gently now in a different voice, a voice Gawain thought he knew from elsewhere. 'No, we shall not fight, you and I. We are friends. Do you not recognize me?' And as he spoke, the green of him vanished, his form changed, and he became the lord of the castle. Gawain was speechless.

'I don't understand any of this,' said Gawain, lowering his sword.

'You will,' said the lord of the castle. 'You will. Twice I held back my axe and drew no blood. That was because you twice kept your promise to me back in the castle, first with the one kiss my wife gave you, and then with the two kisses also. I see you remember it well. But Gawain, the third time, you deceived me. Yes, I had the three kisses she gave you, but she gave you something else as well, didn't she? She gave you a favour to wear, a green belt, a magic belt with power to save your skin, so she said. You see, she told me everything. I knew every word that passed between you. But you never gave the belt to me. You never said a word about it. And for that, I cut you. Because you kept your promise twice, the cut is not too deep, I hope. Had it not been for that, then I can tell you, your head would be lying there at my feet, your life's blood pouring out on the grass.'

'I feel sick with shame,' said Gawain, taking off the green belt and offering it to him.

'No need, Gawain. The belt was a little thing, a little sin. No one is perfect, but you, my friend, are as close to perfect as I have ever met. Keep the belt so that you do not forget us, nor what has happened here. But I'm afraid it's just an ordinary belt; it has no all-powerful magic.'

'After what I did, I do not deserve such kindness,' said Gawain.

'Nonsense.' The lord of the castle took him warmly by the shoulders. 'You wished only to live. What man faced

with death does not wish to live, tell me that? Come, Gawain. I've enough of this dank and dismal place. Let's go back to the castle and feast some more. I'm glad it's over. And I'm sick to death of being green. We'll go home and roast the boar.'

'I'm tempted,' said Gawain. 'But I have another promise to keep. I'd better be on my way home to Camelot, where my duty lies. If I don't get back soon, they'll think I'm dead—as by rights I ought to be. But before I go, tell me something. How were you able to turn yourself green as you did? How could you ride off with your head under your arm? And how was it that there wasn't a single drop of blood when I cut it off?'

'You deserve to know everything, and you shall,' said the lord of the castle. 'Mine is a strange story, but a true one, nonetheless. My name is Sir Bernlak, Knight of the Lake. It was the Lady Nimue, the Lady of the Lake, who enchanted me in this way and sent me to Camelot to test the courage of King Arthur and his knights, to find out if all the good things we had heard were true. I will tell her that there is at least one knight who is as noble as they say, and as brave and gentle too.' The two friends embraced, blessed each other, and parted.

Some weeks later, Gawain arrived back home to Camelot. He told them his story and showed the scar on his neck, and as final proof of the truth of his tale, he held up the green belt interwoven with gold thread. He need not have done so, for, knowing Gawain as everyone there did, no one seated at the Round Table ever doubted a word of it.

Acknowledgements

The following stories were commissioned for *TreeTops Greatest Stories*, *Myths and Legends,* and *Oxford Reading Tree Traditional Tales* collections and are reprinted by permission of the Author and Illustrator unless otherwise stated:

Authors

Thor and the Stolen Hammer and *Vulcan and the Fabulous Throne*
  © Tony Bradman 2014

Finn MacCool and the Giant's Causeway © John Dougherty 2011

Icarus © Susan Gates 2016

Mulan © Michaela Morgan 2011

The Legend of Robin Hood and *Hercules the Hero* © Michaela Morgan 2014

Gawain and the Green Knight © Michael Morpurgo 2018

The Giant of Mont Saint-Michel and *The Lambton Worm* © Jeanne Willis 2016

Illustrators

The Giant of Mont Saint-Michel © Nicolás Aznárez 2016

The Legend of Robin Hood © Mark Beech 2014

Gawain and the Green Knight © Joanna Carey 2018

Finn MacCool and the Giant's Causeway © Lee Cosgrove 2011

Mulan © Steve Dorado 2011

The Lambton Worm © Pierre Kleinhouse 2016

Vulcan and the Fabulous Throne © Andrés Martínez Ricci 2014

Thor and the Stolen Hammer and *Hercules the Hero* © Glen McBeth 2014

Icarus © Joe Todd-Stanton 2016

Additional artwork and title typography © Nathan Collins 2016